Canal boat Cat

Written by Tony Langham
Illustrated by Lynne Willey

Heinemann

Chapter 1

Tabitha was a travelling cat. She was always on the move. She was always looking for new places to go and new people to see.

One day Tabitha got on a big ship without anyone seeing her and went all the way to Amsterdam.

In Amsterdam there are lots of canals.
One day a boy called Dirk was sitting
by a canal trying to catch some fish.
Dirk was just throwing his fishing line
into the water when he saw Tabitha.

She was walking along the canal path
when a man on a bicycle went by.
He was riding very fast and Tabitha
tried to get out of his way. As she
jumped to one side she fell into
the canal.

Tabitha was very scared. She couldn't swim and she started to go under the water.

Dirk had been watching Tabitha so he jumped up and picked up his fishing net.

He ran over to Tabitha and carefully lifted her out of the water.
'Poor thing,' he said. 'You had better come home with me.'

Dirk lived in a house boat on the canal.
He climbed on to the boat with Tabitha
in his arms. His mother helped him to
dry Tabitha with a towel. Then they
gave her some milk.

'Meow,' went Tabitha.

'Can she stay, Mama?' asked Dirk.

'Only if she's good,' said his mother.

Tabitha was happy to stay on the boat
with Dirk and his mother and father.
They were very kind to her.
Dirk fed her every day, and sometimes
he let her sleep on his bed.

And when Dirk went out on his bicycle
Tabitha would jump into his basket
and go with him.

Then one day Dirk's mother came
home with some fish from the market.
She put the fish on the table and went
off to get some water. The fish smelled
so good that Tabitha jumped up on to
the table and ate it all up.

'What do you think you're doing?'
shouted Dirk's mother when she came
back into the room. 'That fish was for
our dinner. You bad cat. Get out!
Get out! And don't come back!'
She chased Tabitha off the boat.

When Dirk came home from school
he was very sad to find Tabitha gone.
'I told you that cat could only stay
with us if she was good!' said his
mother.
Dirk wondered if he would ever see
Tabitha again.

Chapter 2

After she had run away from the canal boat Tabitha went off to look around Amsterdam. There was so much to see. There were lots of bridges, boats and old houses, and lots and lots of bicycles.

13

Soon Tabitha came to a busy street.
A tram stopped right by her. Tabitha
had walked a long way so she got on
the tram for a ride.

Lots of people got on the tram too.
'Look, a cat is having a ride on
the tram,' said a little girl when she
saw Tabitha.

The driver turned round and shouted
at Tabitha, 'Get off my tram. We
can't have cats on here. Shoo! Shoo!'

Tabitha jumped off the tram and ran
into a big building. It was full of
very old paintings. Lots of people were
looking at the paintings so Tabitha
sat and looked at them too. One of
the paintings was of a little boy.
It looked just like Dirk. Tabitha
wondered if Dirk was missing her.
She decided that she would go back to
the canal boat to see him.

Chapter 3

It was very late by the time Tabitha found her way back to Dirk's boat.

Dirk and his mother and father were in bed. The door was shut so Tabitha jumped on to the roof and soon she was fast asleep.

In the middle of the night Tabitha
woke up. She could smell smoke.
It was coming from the kitchen window.
Tabitha started to run up and down
the boat.
'MEOW! MEOW! MEOW!' she went, as
loudly as she could.
But no one woke up.

Then Tabitha saw a bell near a door.
She jumped up and got hold of
the rope.
DING! DONG! DING! DONG!
went the bell.
Tabitha held on as hard as she could.
DING! DONG! DING! DONG!

At last Dirk and his mother and father
woke up. They saw Tabitha by the bell
and they saw smoke coming from
the kitchen.

'Quick!' shouted Dirk's father.
'Off the boat, off, off!'
Dirk took Tabitha in his arms and
jumped off the boat.

Soon the street was full of people, and they all helped Dirk's father to put out the fire with buckets of water from the canal. There was smoke everywhere but the boat was safe.

'It was the cat that woke us up,' said Dirk.

'Yes,' said his mother. 'She is a very clever cat.'

The next day a television reporter
came to see Dirk and his mother and
father. She wanted to know what had
happened. Dirk told them how Tabitha
had saved them.

That night Dirk and his mother and father were watching the news on the television. There was a report about the fire.

'See Tabitha,' said Dirk, 'now everyone knows what a clever cat you are.'
But when he turned round, Tabitha was not there.

Tabitha was already walking off down the canal. She was off somewhere new. She never stayed in one place for long because Tabitha was a travelling cat.